CELEBRATING

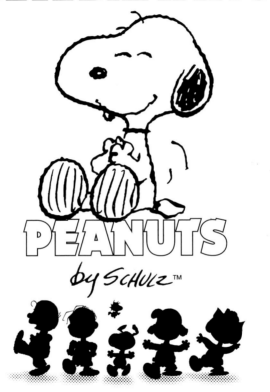

PEANUTS

by SCHULZ™

RAVETTE PUBLISHING

This edition published by Ravette Publishing 2011.

ISBN: 978-1-84161-338-3

PEANUTS Through The Years

Who could have known that a cartoon strip drawn by Sparky Schulz and launched in just seven newspapers on 2nd October 1950, would impact the world for decades to come.

FIRST PEANUTS STRIP

The strip ran until 13th February 2000, the day after Charles Schulz's death at the age of 77.

Now one of the world's most influential and well written cartoons, the strip appears in 2,600 newspapers in 68 countries and entertains an estimated daily readership of 350 million, appealing to children and adults of all ages.

The comic strip is uniquely intimate to Charles Schulz. Snoopy was based on Schulz's childhood dog Spike, Linus was a childhood friend and Charlie Brown a colleague at art school.

In a culture obsessed with winners, Peanuts gave us inspirational characters who never won, but never gave up.

Despite always trying his hardest, Charlie Brown would play baseball knowing victory was less likely

than Linus giving up his security blanket; his attempts to fly a kite always ended up with it getting stuck or gobbled up by 'the kite-eating tree', but he still continued trying to fly it, and his eternal trust and faith in Lucy, who always let him down when she pulled the football away as he was about to kick it, never diminished.

Snoopy, on the other hand refused to take his role seriously as the devoted dog who greets his master when he returns home from school. Preferring to role play, he would embrace each of the characters he chose to portray with great intensity.

Celebrating Peanuts
is a special tribute to Snoopy and the Peanuts Gang.

Containing a selection of some of the best illustrations and strips from the last 60 years, this gift book is a must-have collection for every Peanuts fanatic.

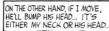

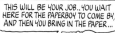

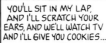

CHARLIE BROWN SAYS HIS ELBOW HURTS SO MUCH HE MAY NEVER BE ABLE TO PITCH AGAIN..

OH, WELL, HE WASN'T MUCH OF A PITCHER ANYWAY..

7-15

© 1996 United Feature Syndicate, Inc.

BOY, THE SNOW IS COMING DOWN HEAVIER THAN EVER..

WHAT WE NEED IS SOMEONE TO GO OUT TO THE MAILBOX...

1-6-98

SOMEONE WHO DOESN'T MAKE A BIG DEAL OUT OF EVERYTHING.

I DON'T SUPPOSE YOUR DOG WANTS TO COME OUT AND PLAY..

NO, I DON'T SUPPOSE HE DOES

I SUPPOSE IT WAS A WASTE OF TIME TO ASK..

I SUPPOSE IT WAS

DO YOU SUPPOSE I MIGHT ASK AGAIN TOMORROW?

I SUPPOSE YOU MIGHT

I SUPPOSE YOU COULD GUESS WHO THAT WAS..

I SUPPOSE I COULD..

IF IT DOESN'T STOP RAINING, I WON'T BE ABLE TO GO OUT AND GET YOUR DOG DISH..

SO I'LL MAKE THE SUPREME SACRIFICE..I'LL PUT ON MY RAIN OUTFIT AND BRAVE THE ELEMENTS!

AFTERWARDS WE CAN HAVE THE AWARDING OF MEDALS..

7-29

PEANUTS

HERE I AM RETURNING FROM HAVING HAD LUNCH WITH THREE AIRLINE STEWARDESSES

WE HAD A GREAT LUNCH... I ENTERTAINED THEM WITH STORIES OF MY WORLD WAR I EXPERIENCES...

WOODSTOCK IS MAD BECAUSE HE DIDN'T GET TO GO ALONG..

AIRLINE STEWARDESSES ARE NOT INTERESTED IN SOMEONE WHO FLIES UPSIDE DOWN!

PEANUTS

SNOOPY'S AT THE VET'S?

YES, HE HAD TO STAY THERE OVERNIGHT FOR X-RAYS..

BUT THEY'LL KEEP HIM IN A CAGE OR SOMETHING, WON'T THEY? HOW WILL HE EVER STAND IT?

HERE'S THE WORLD WAR I FLYING ACE SITTING IN AN ENEMY PRISON CELL...

HERE'S THE WORLD WAR I FLYING ACE BRINGING HIS SOPWITH CAMEL IN FOR A LANDING...

I'M EXHAUSTED...THIS STUPID WAR IS TOO MUCH...

I NEED A NIGHT OF REVELRY... I NEED TO FORGET..

I SHALL GO INTO THE VILLAGE AND QUAFF A FEW ROOT BEERS..

PERHAPS SOME DARK-HAIRED LASS WILL SHARE MY TABLE..

HMM... I'LL HAVE TO WATCH WHAT I SAY TONIGHT, AND NOT BECOME TOO TALKATIVE..

SPIES!

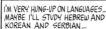

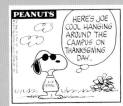

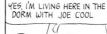

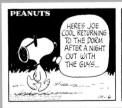

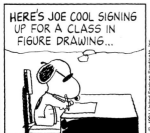

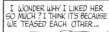

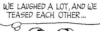

 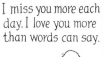   

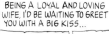

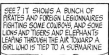

PEANUTS
She wanted to live in Canada.

He wanted to live in Mexico. Thus, they parted.

Years later, when asked the reason, she replied simply,

"I just didn't like his latitude!"

PEANUTS
Dear Contributor,

We think your new story is magnificent.

We want to print it in our next issue, and will pay you One Thousand dollars.

P.S. April Fool!

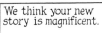

PEANUTS

PEANUTS
YOU'LL NEVER BE A GOOD THEOLOGIAN

YOU'RE TOO **DOGMATIC!**
HAHAHAHA!

BONK!

I HATE JOKES LIKE THAT!

This is my new typewriter

It has many typefaces.

IT CAN ALSO *cross out* mistakes.

Joe Ceremony was very short.

When he entered a room, everyone had to be warned not to stand on Ceremony.

HAHAHAHA!

I'M A GREAT ADMIRER OF MY OWN WRITING

Gentlemen,
Regarding the recent rejection slip you sent me.

I think there might have been a misunderstanding.

What I really wanted was for you to publish my story, and send me fifty thousand dollars.

Didn't you realize that?

Dear Santa Claus,

OKAY, NOW YOU TELL ME WHAT YOU WANT HIM TO BRING YOU, AND I'LL PUT IT IN THE LETTER...

WHAT COLOR?

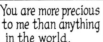

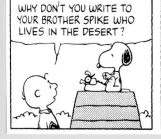

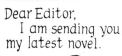

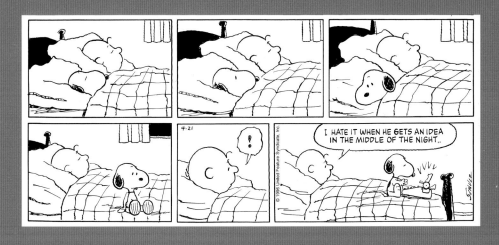

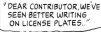

"I will always wait for you," she said. "I'm not going anyplace," he said.

5-7

"If you don't go anyplace, I can't wait for you," she said.

THAT'S THE DUMBEST THING I'VE EVER READ!

© 1998 United Feature Syndicate, Inc.

I'LL ADD SOME FOOTNOTES..

What a writer should know...

7-6

© 1999 United Feature Syndicate, Inc.

NEVER LEAN BACK TO READ WHAT YOU'VE WRITTEN..

The Dog Who Never Did Anything

"You stay home now," they said, "and be a good dog."

So he stayed home, and was a good dog.

© 1999 United Feature Syndicate, Inc.

Then he decided to be even a better dog so he barked at everyone who went by.

And he even chased the neighbor's cats.

"What's happened to you?" they said. "You used to be such a good dog."

11-21

So he stopped barking and chasing cats, and everyone said, "You're a good dog."

The moral is, "Don't do anything, and you'll be a good dog."

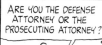

GUESS WHAT, CHUCK! MISS TENURE ACCUSED ME OF STEALING HER BOX OF GOLD STARS...

12-2

THAT'S HARD TO BELIEVE..

© 1977 United Feature Syndicate, Inc.

YOU'RE NOT KIDDING, CHUCK! IS MY STUPID ATTORNEY AROUND THERE ANY PLACE?

YES, HE'S RIGHT HERE...

"CURSE ON ALL LAWS BUT THOSE WHICH LOVE HAS MADE!"

SCHULZ

WHY WOULD I TAKE A BOX OF GOLD STARS, CHUCK?

© 1977 United Feature Syndicate, Inc.

MAYBE MISS TENURE WASN'T ACCUSING YOU... MAYBE SHE WAS JUST ASKING...

I DON'T KNOW... I THINK I'M JUST GONNA NEED A GOOD ATTORNEY

12-3

"GIVE ME THE MAKING OF THE SONGS OF A NATION, AND I CARE NOT WHO MAKES ITS LAWS"

SCHULZ

YOU THINK A BOW TIE AND A BRIEFCASE MAKES YOU OLIVER WENDELL HOLMES?

YOU WOULDN'T KNOW AN OBJECTION FROM A JURY BOX!

5-19

© 1980 United Feature Syndicate, Inc.

TAKE THAT, AND WRITE IT ON YOUR LATEX GUMMED, CANARY YELLOW, EIGHT AND A HALF BY FOURTEEN LEGAL PAD!

HOW TO HURT AN ATTORNEY'S FEELINGS

SCHULZ

I'VE READ A LOT ABOUT ABRAHAM LINCOLN WHEN HE WAS AN ATTORNEY...

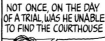
NOT ONCE, ON THE DAY OF A TRIAL, WAS HE UNABLE TO FIND THE COURTHOUSE

LIFE WAS SIMPLER THEN!

SCHULZ   12-2

© 1980 United Feature Syndicate, Inc.

HERE'S THE WORLD FAMOUS LAWYER LEAVING THE COURTHOUSE

THE JUDGE CALLED ME A NIGMENOG, A BOWYER AND A SNAFFLER!

I GUESS THAT'S WHY YOU GO TO LAW SCHOOL

..SO YOU KNOW WHAT YOU'RE BEING CALLED!

THEY WON'T LET YOU PLAY BASEBALL ON THAT VACANT LOT ANY MORE? THAT'S RIDICULOUS!!

YOU KNOW WHAT YOU NEED? YOU NEED A GOOD ATTORNEY!

I SAID A "GOOD" ATTORNEY!

SIGH

THE COURT WILL NOT AID THOSE WHO HAVE COMMITTED ILLEGAL ACTS IN A MATTER...

..AND THEN ASK THE COURT'S HELP TO RECOVER FOR ANY INJURY THEY MAY HAVE SUFFERED AS A RESULT THEREOF!

RATS!

I CAN'T BELIEVE IT... YOU'RE HELPING ME WITH MY HOMEWORK!

IT'S BETTER THAN HAVING YOUR ATTORNEY SUE ME..

I WON'T NEED YOU AFTER ALL, ATTORNEY.. WE'VE DECIDED TO SETTLE OUT OF COURT...

HOW WILL I EVER PAY FOR MY NEW BRIEFCASE?

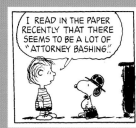

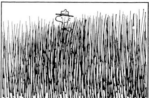

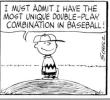

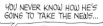

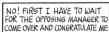

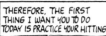

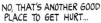

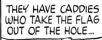

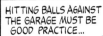

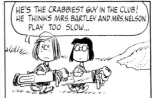

MOLLY VOLLEY IS ON THE PHONE

SHE WANTS YOU TO BE HER PARTNER IN THE SPRING MIXED DOUBLES TENNIS TOURNAMENT

3-24

© 1986 United Feature Syndicate, Inc.

SHE'S THE ONE WITH THE FAT FACE, THE FAT BODY AND THE FAT LEGS...

SCHULZ

SHE WANTS TO KNOW IF YOU REMEMBER HER..

VAGUELY..

YOU THOUGHT I'D FORGET THE CHOCOLATE CHIP COOKIES, DIDN'T YOU?

NOW, THE QUESTION IS, DO WE EAT THEM BETWEEN SETS..

3-26

OR DO WE EAT THEM BETWEEN GAMES?

HOW ABOUT BETWEEN POINTS?

© 1986 United Feature Syndicate, Inc.

LOOK, IT'S AN ATHLETIC AWARD..

EACH YEAR THEY GIVE AN AWARD TO THE INJURED ATHLETE WHO HAS MADE THE BEST COMEBACK..

© 1986 United Feature Syndicate, Inc.

REMEMBER WHEN YOU GOT HURT PLAYING HOCKEY?

1-31

WELL, YOU DID IT..

YOU WON THE AWARD FOR THE ATHLETE WHO MADE NO COMEBACK AT ALL!

SCHULZ

© 1988 United Feature Syndicate, Inc.

WELL, HOW WAS THE KITE-FLYING?

I HATE TO ADMIT IT, BUT I JUST SAW SOMETHING THAT MADE ME FEEL REAL GOOD..

3-27

6-30

A GOOD GOLFER REALLY NEEDS TWO CADDIES..

ONE TO CARRY HIS CLUBS...

AND ONE TO CARRY HIS SANDWICH!

© 1989 United Feature Syndicate, Inc.

WHERE'S EVERYBODY GOING? THIS IS ONLY A SHOWER!

C'MON! WE NEED THE PRACTICE! ARE YOU AFRAID OF A LITTLE RAIN?!!

3-8

© 1990 United Feature Syndicate, Inc.

When Schulz announced his retirement
for health reasons in December 1999,
Peanuts was in more than 2,600 newspapers worldwide.

He died shortly thereafter,
on Saturday 12th February 2000,
just hours before the final Peanuts Sunday strip
appeared in newspapers.

Other PEANUTS Gift Books available ...

	ISBN	PRICE
A Friend is ... forever	978-1-84161-213-3	£4.99
Best Friends ... understand sharing	978-1-84161-258-4	£4.99
Happiness is ... a warm puppy	978-1-84161-211-9	£4.99
Love is ... walking hand in hand	978-1-84161-212-6	£4.99
Peanuts Guide to Life Book 1	978-1-84161-268-3	£4.99
Peanuts Guide to Life Book 2	978-1-84161-269-0	£4.99
Peanuts Guide to Life Book 3	978-1-84161-287-4	£4.99
Security is ... a thumb and a blanket	978-1-84161-210-2	£4.99
True Love is ... complete trust	978-1-84161-259-1	£4.99
It's Your First Crush, Charlie Brown!	978-1-84161-295-9	£7.99

HOW TO ORDER:

Please send a cheque/postal order in £ sterling, made payable to 'Ravette Publishing'
for the cover price of the book/s and allow the following for post & packing ...

UK & BFPO	70p for the first book & 40p per book thereafter
Europe & Eire	£1.30 for the first book & 70p per book thereafter
Rest of the world	£2.20 for the first book & £1.10 per book thereafter

RAVETTE PUBLISHING LTD
PO Box 876, Horsham, West Sussex   RH12 9GH
Tel: 01403 711443   Fax: 01403 711554   Email: ingrid@ravettepub.co.uk

Prices and availability are subject to change without prior notice.